GW00857354

this book belongs to

_____

a gift from

_____

_____

D A T E

Moon Cradle
LULLABIES

PAT DONLON

Director of the National Library, she has had a long-term interest in children's literature. She organised and taught the Children's Literature Course at University College Dublin for several years, and she has published widely in the area. She is well known as a lecturer and broadcaster.

MADDY GLAS

Studied literature at the Sorbonne University, Paris, and prepared her doctoral thesis on the subject of Children's Literature in Ireland. Now living in the Netherlands, she was born in Mali and spent many childhood years in Senegal.

Moon Cradle's rocking and rocking
Where never a cloud goes by
Silently rocking, rocking
The Moon Cradle out in the sky.

Padraic Colum

MOON CRADLE

LULLABIES

AND DANDLING SONGS FROM IRELAND
WITH OLD CHILDHOOD FAVOURITES

Chosen by
PAT DONLON
AND
MADDY GLAS

Illustrations
DONALD TESKEY

THE O'BRIEN PRESS
DUBLIN

☆ *Contents* ☆

A Note for Readers   11

SLEEPYHEAD

How Many Miles to Babylon?   14

To Bed, To Bed   15

Dance to Your Daddy   16

Summertime   17

Hush Little Baby   18

LULLABIES AND SONGS FROM IRELAND

The Winter Night   22

Lullaby   23

The Rathlin Cradle Song   24

Hup, Hup, My Little Horse   25

Connemara Cradle Song   26

An Irish Lullaby   28

Sleep Song   30

A Cradle Song   32

DANDLING SONGS FROM THE IRISH

Tá'n Coileach ag Fógairt an Lae/ 34

The Cock Is Announcing the Day 37

Oró Mo Bháidín 38 / Oh Row My Little Boat 41

Éiníní 42 / Little Birdies 45

'Ceol,' Ars' an t-Asal / Donkey Music 46

Cuirfimid Deandaí 48 / The Dandling Song 51

Thugamar Féin an Samhradh Linn / The Summer 52

HUSH-A-BYE, BABY ...

Hush-a-bye, Baby 56

Sleep, Baby, Sleep! 57

The Rocking Carol 58

Lullaby 60

The Evening Is Coming 62

Safe in Bed 64

First published 1991 by The O'Brien Press Ltd.,
20 Victoria Road, Dublin 6, Ireland.

Copyright © the collection – Pat Donlon and Maddy Glas;
© translations from Irish – Ide ní Laoghaire;
© the illustrations – The O'Brien Press Ltd.

10 9 8 7 6 5 4 3 2 1

All rights reserved. No part of this book may be reproduced or
utilised in any way or by any means, electronic or mechanical, including
photocopying, recording or by any information storage and retrieval
system without permission in writing from the publisher. This book
may not be sold as a remainder, bargain book or at a reduced price
without permission in writing from the publisher.

British Library Cataloguing in Publication Data
A catalogue record for this book is
available from the British Library.
ISBN 0-86278-272-4

Typeset at The O'Brien Press
Music: Seton Music Graphics Ltd, Bantry, Co. Cork
Design and layout: Ide ní Laoghaire & Michael O'Brien
Separations: The City Office, Dublin
Printing: Colour Books Ltd, Dublin

Acknowledgements: The authors and publisher thank Walton's for
permission to reproduce 'The Connemara Cradle Song', and all
those who gave permission to use copyright material.
Every effort has been made to trace copyright holders, but
if any infringement has occurred the publishers request the
holders of such copyright to contact them immediately.

The O'Brien Press receives assistance from
The Arts Council / An Chomhairle Ealaíon

From the moment a baby is born our instinct is to croon and cuddle, to rock and sing to the tiny child. The first songs a child hears are lullabies and baby songs – songs often sung before bedtime as baby is bounced and dandled before settling down for the night.

This little gathering of baby songs and lullabies brings together some very old songs and rhymes – so old their origin is lost – some unusual, some new, and all, we believe, beautiful. Poets and children have a very special link – both love strange sounds and magical words, and so, many of the lullabies in this book are poems and were written to be read, not sung, but the sounds are soothing and rhythmic and may give comfort and pleasure to parents and children alike. The songs from the Irish language belong to a rural tradition. The translations here are extremely loose, keeping, we hope, the spirit and rhythm of the songs. No attempt has been made at literal translation. In some cases, for simplicity, only part of the tune has been used.

It is never too early to begin reading to children and poetry and music learnt in this special way creates a bond between parent and child and between child and poet that lasts a very long time.

Pat Donlon and Maddy Glas

In memory of
EILEEN
and
to welcome my godchild
ELIZABETH

Pat Donlon

☆ SLEEPYHEAD ☆

How Many Miles to Babylon?

How many miles to Babylon?
Three score and ten.
Can I get there by candlelight?
Yes, and back again.

To Bed, to Bed

'To bed, to bed,' says Sleepyhead,
'Time enough,' says Slow,
'Put on the pot,' says Greedy Guts,
'We'll eat before we go.'

Dance to Your Daddy

Dance to your daddy,
My little babby,
Dance to your daddy,
My little lamb.

You shall have a fishy
In a little dishy,
You shall have a fishy
When the boat comes in.

Summertime

Summertime and the livin' is easy,
Fish are jumpin'
And the cotton is high,
Oh, your Daddy's rich,
And your Ma is good lookin',
So hush, little baby, don' you cry.

One of these mornin's
You goin' to rise up singin',
Then you'll spread your wings
And you'll take the sky.
But till that mornin'
There's a nothin' can harm you,
With Daddy an' Mammy standin' by.

Hush, Little Baby

Hush, little baby, don't say a word,
Papa's gonna buy you a mockingbird.
If that mockingbird won't sing,
Papa's gonna buy you a diamond ring.

If that diamond ring turns brass,
Papa's gonna buy you a looking glass.
If that looking glass gets broke,
Papa's gonna buy you a billy goat.

If that billy goat won't pull,
Papa's gonna buy you a cart and bull.
If that cart and bull turn over,
Papa's gonna buy you a dog named Rover.

If that dog named Rover won't bark,
Papa's gonna buy you a horse and cart.
If that horse and cart fall down,
You'll still be the sweetest baby in town.

Freely

Hush, lit-tle ba - by, don't say a word,

Pa-pa's gon-na buy you a mock-ing bird.

If that mock - ing bird won't sing,

Pa-pa's gon-na buy you a dia - mond ring.

LULLABIES AND SONGS
☆ FROM IRELAND ☆

The Winter Night

Wind in the Wicklow hills tonight,
Wind in the hills, and rain;
The doors are closed and the curtain's drawn
And winter's here again.

The leaves are down, the trees are bare,
The streams are wide and deep,
And what's to do for a sleepy head
But go to bed and sleep.

John Irvine

Lullaby

Husheen the herons are crying,
Away in the rain and the sleet,
Flying and flying and flying
With never a rest to their feet.

But warm in your coverlet nestle
Wee bird, till the dawn of the day,
Nor dream of the wild wings that wrestle
In the night and the rain and the grey.

Seumas O'Sullivan

The Rathlin Cradle Song

The night is on the dark sea wave
And the boats are on the deep,
But here within the quiet room
My treasure lies asleep.

Oh! may Our Lady come and bless
The cradle where you lie,
And wind and wave, and moon and stars,
Shall sing you lullaby.

John Irvine

Hup, Hup, My Little Horse

Hup, hup, my little horse,
Hup, hup, again, sir:
How many miles to Dublin town?
Three score and ten, sir.

Here we go up, up, up,
And here we go down, down, down,
And now we go this and that way
And high for Dublin town.

Connemara Cradle Song

On wings of the wind o'er the dark rolling deep,
Angels are coming to watch o'er thy sleep,
Angels are coming to watch over thee,
So list to the wind coming over the sea.

Chorus:
Hear the wind blow, dear,
Hear the wind blow,
Lean your head over
And hear the wind blow.

On wings of the sailing way out in the blue,
Laden with herrin' of silvery hue,
Silver the herrin' and silver the sea,
And soon there'll be silver for baby and me.
　　　Chorus.

Delia Murphy

Gentle lilting style

On wings of the wind o'er the dark roll - ing

deep, ____ An - gels are com - ing to watch o'er thy

sleep, ____ An - gels are com - ing to watch o - ver

thee, ____ So list to the wind com - ing o - ver the

Chorus

sea. ____ Hear the wind blow, dear, Hear the wind

blow, Lean your head o - ver And hear the wind blow. ____

An Irish Lullaby

I'd rock my own sweet childie to rest
In a cradle of gold, on a bough of the willow,
To the *shoheen sho!* of the wind of the west
And the *lulla lo!* of the soft sea-billow.
Sleep, baby dear! sleep without fear!
Mother is here beside your pillow.

Moderate tempo

I'd rock my own sweet chil - die to rest In a cra - dle of gold, on a bough of the wil - low, To the sho - heen sho of the wind of the west, And the lull - a - lo of the soft____ sea - bil____ low. Sleep, ba - by dear, sleep with - out fear! Mo - ther is here____ be - side____ your pil - low. Sleep, ba - by dear, sleep with - out fear! Mo - ther is here be - side your pil - low.

Sleep Song

My child, the new moon is a cradle,
Soft winds rock each baby star;
That peaceful murmur is their sleep song,
Coming from afar;
Sleep, sleep, my babe!
Sleep, sleep, my babe!

O when old north wind rocks their cradle,
Baby stars fall from the sky;
But gentle breezes lift them lightly,
Singing lullaby!
Lull-ula-by!
Lull-ula-by!

Quite slow, smoothly

My child, the new moon is___ a cra - dle,

Soft winds rock each ba - by star; That

peace - ful mur - mur is___ their sleep___ song,

Com - ing from___ a - far;___

Sleep, sleep___ my babe!___

Sleep, sleep___ my babe!___

A Cradle Song

O, men from the fields!
Come gently within.
Tread softly, softly,
O! men coming in.

Mavourneen is going
From me and from you,
Where Mary will fold him
With mantle of blue!

From reek of the smoke
And cold of the floor,
And the peering of things
Across the half-door.

O, men from the fields!
Soft, softly come through –
Mary puts round him
Her mantle of blue.

Padraic Colum

DANDLING SONGS
FROM
☆ THE IRISH ☆

Tá'n Coileach ag Fógairt an Lae

Tá'n coileach ag fógairt an lae
Tá'n coileach ag fógairt an lae
Tá'n mhuc ag an doras ag iarraidh é 'oscailt –
Tá'n coileach ag fógairt an lae.

Tá'n coileach ag fógairt an lae
Tá'n coileach ag fógairt an lae
Tá'n chearc is a há ina gcoladh go sámh –
Tá'n coileach ag fógairt an lae.

Tá'n coileach ag fógairt an lae
Tá'n coileach ag fógairt an lae
Tá'n chaora is na huain ina dtoirchim suain –
Tá'n coileach ag fógairt an lae.

Quite fast, lively

Tá'n coil - each ag fó - gairt an lae_____ Tá'n
The cock is an - nounc - ing the day_____ The

coil - each ag fóg - airt an lae_____ Tá'n
cock is an - noun - cing the day_____ The

mhuc ag an dor - as ag iar - raidh é 'os - cailt Tá'n
horse in the barn is just start - ing to neigh And the

coil - each ag fó - gairt an lae._____
cock is an - noun - cing the day._____

The Cock Is Announcing the Day

The cock is announcing the day
The cock is announcing the day
The horse in the barn is just starting to neigh –
And the cock is announcing the day!

The cock is announcing the day
The cock is announcing the day
The hen and her brood are all sleeping away –
But the cock is announcing the day!

The cock is announcing the day
The cock is announcing the day
The sheep and the lambs are still dreaming away –
But the cock is announcing the day!

The cock is announcing the day
The cock is announcing the day
The donkey's asleep but he'll soon start to bray –
And the cock is announcing the day!

Óró Mo Bháidín

Óró mo bháidín ag snámh ar an gcuan,
Óró mo bháidín,
Faighimis na maidí agus téimis chun siúil,
Óró mo bháidín.

Curfá:
Óró mo churraichín ó, óró mo bháidín,
Óró mo churraichín ó, óró mo bháidín.

Crochfaidh mé seolta is gabhfaidh mé siar,
Óró mo bháidín,
Is go hOíche Fhéile Eoin ní thiochfaidh mé aniar,
Óró mo bháidín.
    Curfá.

Nach lúfar í ag iomramh soir agus siar,
Óró mo bháidín.
A sárú ní bhfaighidh tú ó Árainn go Cliar,
Óró mo bháidín.
    Curfá.

Quite fast

Ó - ró mo bháid - ín ag snámh ar an gcuan,
Oh row my little boat, out in the bay,

Ó - ró mo bháid - ín,
Oh row my boat - een,

Faigh - imis na mai - dí is téi - mis chun siúil
Gath - er the oars and then we'll a - way

Ó - ró mo bháid - ín.
Oh row my boat - een.

Curfá / Chorus

Ó - ró mo churr - aich - ín ó,
Oh row my cur - ach - een oh,

Ó - ró mo bháid - ín,
Oh row my boat - een,

Ó - ró mo churr - aich - ín ó,
Oh row my curr - ach - een oh,

Ó - ró mo bháid - ín.
Oh row my boat - een.

Oh Row My Little Boat

Oh row my little boat, out in the bay,
Oh row my boateen,
Gather the oars and then we'll away
Oh row my boateen.

Chorus:
Oh row my curracheen oh,
Oh row my boateen,
Oh row my curracheen oh,
Oh row my boateen.

Up with the sails and off to the west
Oh row my boateen,
Till we come home we will take no rest
Oh row my boateen.
    Chorus.

Off we go sailing here and there,
Oh row my boateen,
The best little boat between Kerry and Clare,
Oh row my boateen.
    Chorus.

Éiní

Éiní, éiní, codalaígí, codalaígí,
Éiní, éiní, codalaígí, codalaígí.

Codalaígí, codalaígí,
Cois an chlaí amuigh, cois an chlaí amuigh,
Codalaígí, codalaígí,
Cois an chlaí amuigh, cois an chlaí amuigh.
Curfá.

An londubh 's an fiach dubh,
Téigí a chodlagh, téigí a chodlagh,
An chéirseach 's an préachán,
Téigí a chodlagh, téigí a chodlagh.
Curfá.

An spideog 's an fhuiseog,
Téigí a chodlagh, téigí a chodlagh,
An dreoilín 's an smóilín,
Téigí a chodlagh, téigí a chodlagh.
Curfá.

Quite slow

Curfá / Chorus

Éin - ín - í, éin - ín - í, cod - al
Lit-tle bird - ies, lit-tle bird - ies, Sleep

aí - gí, cod - al - aí - gí, Éin -
eas - y, sleep eas - y, Lit-tle

ín - í, éin - ín - í, cod - al -
bird - ies, Lit-tle bird - ies, Sleep

aí - gí, cod - al - aí - gí. Cod - al -
eas - y, sleep eas - y. Sleep

aí - gí cod - al - aí - gí Cois an
eas - y, sleep eas - y, In the

chlaí amuigh, cois an chlaí amuigh, Cod - al -
trees and in the breez - es, Sleep

aí - gí, cod - al - aí - gí, Cois an
eas - y, sleep eas - y, In the

chlaí amuigh, cois an chlaí amuigh.
trees and in the breez - es.

Little Birdies

Little birdies, little birdies,
Sleep easy, sleep easy,
Little birdies, little birdies,
Sleep easy, sleep easy.

Sleep easy, sleep easy,
In the trees and in the breezes,
Sleep easy, sleep easy,
In the trees and in the breezes.
Chorus.

Little blackbirds, little ravens,
Off to sleep now, off to sleep now,
Little starlings, little finches,
Off to sleep now, off to sleep now.
Chorus.

Little robins, little skylarks,
Go to sleep now, go to sleep now,
Little wrens and little thrushes,
Go to sleep now, go to sleep now.
Chorus.

'Ceol,' Ars' an t-Asal

'Ceol,' ars' an t-asal
Is é istigh sa ghort,
'Éist le mo ghlórsa
Is é is binne port!
Hí há, hí há, hí ha ha ha ha há!'

Donkey Music

'Oh,' said the donkey
Living in the west,
'Listen to my song now
Isn't it the best!
Hee haw, hee haw, hee ha ha ha ha ha haw!'

Moderate tempo

'Ceol,' ars' an t-as - al Is é is-tigh sa ghort,
'Oh,' said the don - key ___ Liv-ing in the west,

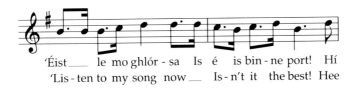

'Éist___ le mo ghlór - sa Is é is bin - ne port! Hí
'Lis - ten to my song now ___ Is - n't it the best! Hee

há, hí há hí ha ha ha ha há!'
haw, hee haw, hee ha ha ha ha haw!'

47

Cuirfimid Deandaí

Cuirfimid deandaí deandaí
Cuirfimid deandaí 'r Mháire
Cuirfimid deandaí deandaí
Bróga 's stocaí bána.

Curfá:
Hóró deamhas is deamhas is
Hóró deamhas go haerach,
Hóró deamhas is deamhas is
Deamhas is deamhas a lao ghil.

Caithfimid suas é suas é
Caithfimid suas an páiste
Caithfimid suas é suas é 's
Tiochfaid sé 'nuas amárach.
Curfá.

Slip jig time

Cuir - fi - mid dean - daí dean - daí,
Here we go dand - ling, dand - ling,

Cuir - fi - mid dean - daí'r Mhái - re,
Here we go dand - ling gai - ly,

Cuir - fi - mid dean - daí dean - daí,
Here we go dand - ling, dand - ling,

Bró - ga's stoc - aí bá - na.
All through the night and day.

Curfá / Chorus

Hó - ró deamhas is deamhas is
Danc - ing up and up, and

Hó - ró deamhas go h-aer - ach,
Up and down all day.

Hó - ró deamhas is deamhas is
Danc - ing up and up

deamhas is deamhas a lao ghil.
Up in the air and a - way!

The Dandling Song

Here we go dandling, dandling,
Here we go dandling gaily,
Here we go dandling, dandling,
All through the night and day!

Chorus:
Dancing up and up, and
Up and down all day.
Dancing up and up –
Up in the air and away!

Here we go bouncing, bouncing,
Up in the air so lightly,
Here we go bouncing, bouncing –
Up as far as the sky!
    Chorus.

Thugamar Féin an Samhradh Linn

Samhradh, samhradh, bainne na ngamhna,
Thugamar féin an samhradh linn,
Samhradh buí na nóinín gléigeal,
Thugamar féin an samhradh linn.

The Summer

Summer, summer, happy and laughing,
Let us all dance the summer away –
Sparkling daisies all through the meadows,
Let us all dance the summer away.

Moderate tempo

Samh - radh, samh - radh, bain - ne na ngamh - na,
Sum - mer, sum - mer, hap - py and laugh - ing,

Thug - a - mar féin an samh - radh linn,
Let us all dance the summer a - way,

Samh - radh buí na nóin - ín gléi - geal,
Spark - ling dais - ies all through the mead - ows,

Thug - a - mar féin an samh - radh linn.
Let us all dance the summer a - way.

☆ HUSH-A-BYE, BABY ☆

Hush-a-bye, Baby

Hush-a-bye, baby,
On the tree top,
When the wind blows
The cradle will rock;
When the bough breaks
The cradle will fall,
Down will come baby,
Cradle and all!

Sleep, Baby, Sleep!

Sleep, baby, sleep!
Thy father watches the sheep.
Thy mother is shaking the dreamland tree,
And down falls a little dream on thee.
Sleep, baby, sleep!

Sleep, baby, sleep!
The large stars are the sheep.
The little stars are the lambs, I guess,
The big round moon is the shepherdess.
Sleep, baby, sleep!

The Rocking Carol

Little Jesus, sweetly sleep, do not stir;
We will lend you
a coat of fur,
We will rock you, rock you, rock you,
We will rock you, rock you, rock you;
See the fur to keep you warm,
Snugly round your tiny form.

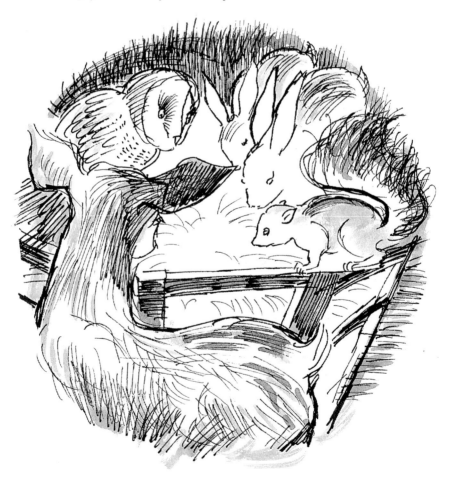

Mary's little baby, sleep, sweetly sleep.
Sleep in comfort, slumber deep;
We will rock you, rock you, rock you,
We will rock you, rock you, rock you;
We will serve you all we can,
Darling, darling, little man.

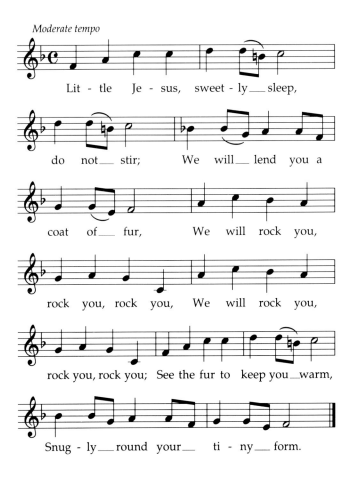

Moderate tempo

Lit - tle Je - sus, sweet - ly __ sleep,

do not __ stir; We will __ lend you a

coat of __ fur, We will rock you,

rock you, rock you, We will rock you,

rock you, rock you; See the fur to keep you __ warm,

Snug - ly __ round your __ ti - ny __ form.

Lullaby

Laugh, laugh,
Laugh gently though –
For leaves do so,
When the great boughs, to and fro,
Cradle the birds on the tops of the trees –
Gently they laugh for the love of these.

Sleep, sleep,
Sleep lightly, though –
For birds do so,
Rocked by great boughs to and fro;
With wind in their feathers, their dreams have wings
And they visit the gardens of fabulous kings.

T. Sturge Moore

The Evening Is Coming

The evening is coming, the sun sinks to rest,
The birds are all flying straight home to their nests,
'Caw, caw,' says the crow as he flies overhead,
It's time little children were going to bed.

Here comes the pony, his work is all done,
Down through the meadow he takes a good run,
Up go his heels – and down goes his head.
It's time little children were going to bed.

Safe in Bed

Matthew, Mark, Luke and John,
Bless the bed that I lie on!
Four corners to my bed,
Four angels there lie spread:
Two at my head,
Two at my feet,
I pray the Lord my soul to keep.